KT-155-375

Willbee the Bumblebee

By

Craig Smith & Maureen Thomson

Illustrated by

Katz Cowley

SCHOLASTIC

Dedicated to William (Willbee) John Thomson. For his cuddles and humour.
A gentle-man in every way, we think of him every day.
And to all the little bees that do such a great job in our gardens and fields.
– Craig Smith & Maureen Thomson

To Clarki~pooh … endless gratty-chewed for your magical input,
inspiration and endless tiddlypoms
– Katz Cowley

This edition published in the UK in 2019 by Scholastic Children's Books
Euston House, 24 Eversholt Street
London NW1 1DB, UK
A division of Scholastic Ltd
www.scholastic.co.uk
London ~ New York ~ Toronto ~ Sydney ~ Auckland
Mexico City ~ New Delhi ~ Hong Kong

First published in 2010 by Scholastic New Zealand Ltd.

Text copyright © Craig Smith and Maureen Thomson, 2007
Illustrations copyright © Katz Crowley, 2010

ISBN 978 1 407196 61 9

All rights reserved
Printed in the UK by CPI Colour Ltd

5 7 9 8 6 4

The moral rights of Craig Smith, Maureen Thomson and
Katz Crowley have been asserted.

Papers used by Scholastic Children's Books
are made from wood grown in sustainable forests.

Willbee, the bumblebee,
lives his life in your garden
so happily.

Up early in the morning
till the evening hour,

flying around
from flower to flower.

Now everybody knows, I suppose,
without bees in your garden, nothing grows.

They take the pollen to where it's supposed to be.

That's how nature works.

Good job, Willbee!

Now bumblebees,
from the day they are
born,

wear a black and yellow jersey
just to keep them
warm,

and Willbee's was special,

it was a
perfect fit,

'cause Willbee's mother
had knitted it.

Willbee was out one sunny day,

unknown to him his jersey had begun to fray,

and his jersey caught
where it was torn ...

right on the end of
a rose's thorn.

And as Willbee flew away, he did not stop,

his jersey unravelled
         from the bottom to the top,

and when he realised this,
         he lost his hum ...

He was showing
the whole garden
his bare bum!

Well, with no jersey,
and being late in the day,

Willbee was so cold
he couldn't fly away.

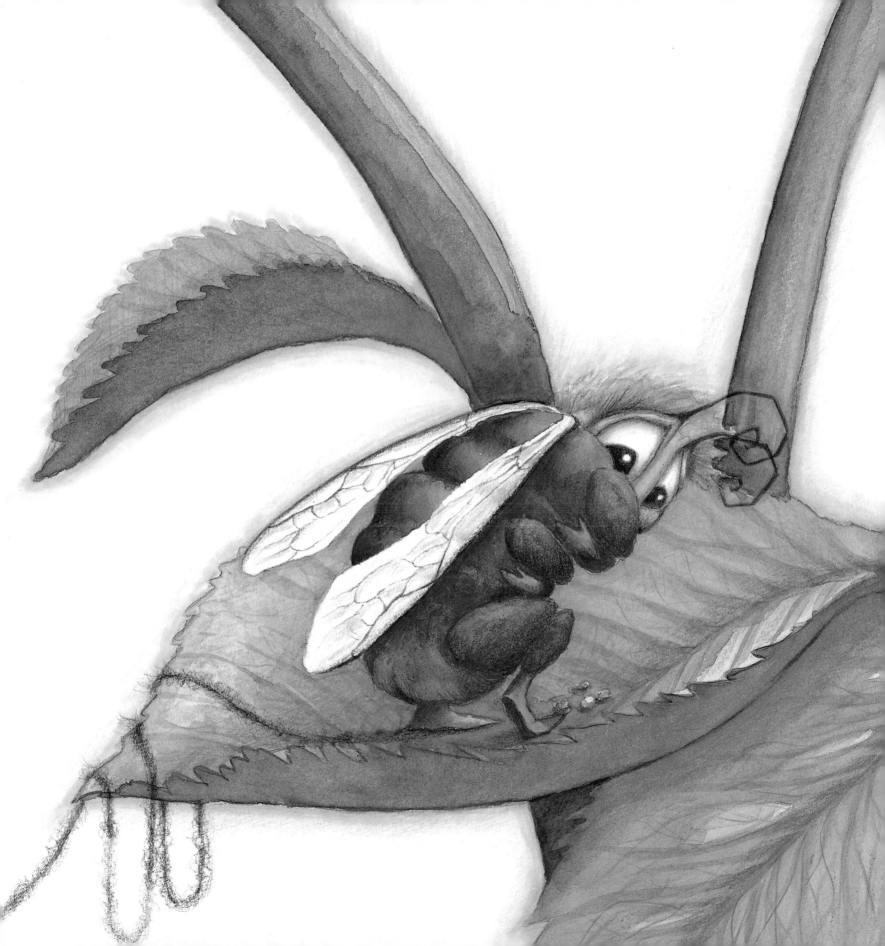

He was frightened,
and all alone.

All he wanted
to do was to
get home.

Now Monica the butterfly,
she flew down;

she told Willbee to
wipe off his frown.

She'd seen
what had happened
and thought she knew
what to do.

She gathered all the wool up,

and off she flew.

With the unravelled wool,
she flew to spider Steve
and asked him for help because she
knew he could weave.

With a twist of his arm,
she had him agree;
he would weave the wool they had
and make a new jersey.

Now spider Steve,
he finished so quickly!

He used a pattern
he'd found in the
Woman's Weekly.

Moni, with a smile,
    she thanked him so,

    but Willbee needed help
        and now she had to go.

She found Willbee where he was last.

She said, "Quick! Put this on ...
really, really fast."

With his new jersey on,
he got back his
hum,

all his bits were warmed up ...
even his
bum!

Willbee hugged Moni
with a big thank you.

He asked her to thank
spider Steve for him too,

but now back to his house
he had to go,

for he knew his mum would worry
'cause she loved him so.

Now on a sunny day in your back yard,
you might still see Willbee, working hard,

from flower to flower, and carefree,
wearing his new

black and yellow jersey.

KT-44 6-774

This one's for you Ma,
Frances Maisie Collins.

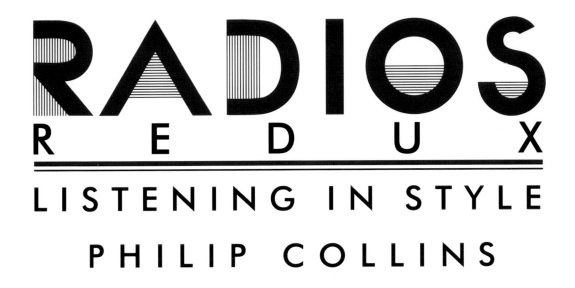

RADIOS
REDUX
LISTENING IN STYLE

PHILIP COLLINS

PHOTOGRAPHY BY
SAM SARGENT

CHRONICLE BOOKS • SAN FRANCISCO

A Fillip Book

Text copyright © 1991 by Philip Collins
Photographs copyright ©1991 by Sam Sargent
All rights reserved. No part of this book may be reproduced in
any form without written permission from the publisher.

Printed in Japan.

Library of Congress Cataloging-in-Publication Data
Collins, Philip, 1944–
    Radios redux : listening in style / Philip Collins.
        p.   cm.
    Includes bibliographical references and index.
    ISBN 0-8118-0099-7 (hardcover) — ISBN 0-8118-0086-5 (softcover)
    1. Radio—Receivers and reception—Collectors and collecting-
-United States.   I. Title.
    TK6563.C563   1992
    S21.348'18'075—dc20   91-34530
                                                       CIP

Half title photograph: "The Selling Fool,"
designed for RCA by Maxfield Parrish, 1926.

Book and cover design: Karen Pike

Distributed in Canada by
Raincoast Books
112 East Third Avenue
Vancouver, B.C. V5T 1C8

10 9 8 7 6 5 4 3 2 1

Chronicle Books
275 Fifth Street
San Francisco, California 94103

"CHANGED ITS NAME TO 'RADIO' AND SET
TO WORK TO AMUSE AND EDIFY THE
WORLD"

SEE YOU ON THE RADIO

See you on the radio . . . I say that every week.
A peculiar phrase, some people think, for anyone to speak.
I've got a piece of mail or two, up on my office shelf,
Complaining that the sentence seems to contradict itself.
"Dear Mr. Osgood," someone wrote, "That sign off is absurd.
Radio is for the ear . . . the song or spoken word.
The medium for seeing is, without a doubt, TV.
We therefore call it 'video.' That's Latin for 'I see.'
So please don't say that anymore. You really should know better."
That's a gentle paraphrase of what was in this viewer's letter.

"Dear Sir," I then wrote back to him, and this was my reply:
"I do believe that you are wrong, and let me tell you why.
I've worked some years in radio, and television, too.
And though it's paradoxical it nonetheless is true
That radio is visual, much moreso than TV.
And there's plenty of good reason why that paradox should be.
You insist that on the radio there are no pictures there.
You say it's only for the ear . . . but I say "au contraire."
There are fascinating pictures on the radio you see,
That are far more picturesque than any pictures on TV.
No television set that's made, no screen that you can find,
Can compare with that of radio: the theater of the mind.
Where the pictures are so vivid, so spectacular and real,
That there isn't any contest, or at least that's how I feel.
The colors are more colorful, the reds and greens and blues
Are more vivid yet more subtle than television's hues.
The dimensions of the radio are truly to be treasured
Infinite the size of screen diagonally measured,
We can whisper in the listener's ear and take him *anywhere*.
And you tell me that I cannot see the audience I touch?
Let me tell you now a secret . . . my experience is such
That although the room I work in may be very plain and small . . .
In a way that's quite miraculous, it isn't small at all.
I am there inside the radio, the one beside the bed.
And it's me you hear when it goes off . . . come on now sleepyhead.
I can see you in the morning . . . I can see you coast to coast
As you sip your glass of orange juice and bite into your toast.
I am with you as you brush your teeth and as you shave your face.

You may think you are alone but I am with you everyplace.
And I see the lines of traffic stretching endlessly for miles.
Not a hundred or a thousand miles . . . a million there must be.
And I'm riding along with them. This is radio you see.
And I'm on the Jersey Turnpike, on the throughway and the Hutch,
And the Eisenhower Expressway helping people keep in touch,
And the California freeways and the Houston traffic funnel.
I may lose you for a little while as you go through the tunnel.
But suddenly I'm there again, some episode to tell,
To nobody's surprise, because they know me very well."

For my voice is with them every day, and when it disappears,
They know it comes right back again, it's been that way for years.
I've been riding with them every day for such a long, long time
They are willing to put up with me when I resort to rhyme.
And that may be the ultimate and quintessential test
That proves beyond the slightest doubt that radio is best.
A friend will always stick with you . . .
though your poems may not scan.
I'll see you on the radio . . . I can, you see, I can.

Charles Osgood

INTRODUCTION

"Hello Chief, this is Jack Benny again. Remember the last time I spoke to you about my missing wallet? Oh, you must remember it, it was five minutes ago! Now look, Chief. I'm willing to offer a reward. Take this down: if the finder of a black wallet containing eight dollars in cash and some important papers returns the money, he can keep the papers."

America laughed. It was an experience shared by millions, coming together to fight the depression and war. Jack Benny, Fibber McGee & Molly, and Amos 'n Andy put a smile on the nation's faces in dark days. The Shadow conjured mysterious, superhuman influences at work. The naive messages from the Lone Ranger and Dick Tracy had a spine of truth, justice, and the American way. Little wonder that, like Woody Allen in his affectionate *Radio Days*, so many of us share a shameless nostalgia for a simpler time. Our youth.

We had heroes, and sponsored programming spawned an unprecedented merchandising operation, the radio premium, that kept us constantly in their confidence. Decoder rings and shake-up mugs abounded. A Buck Rogers ring would glow in the dark when held by an Earthman (but not by a Venusian). A Sky King ring could write underwater. There were a Sergeant Preston totem pole, a Bulldog Drummond magnifying glass, a Lone Ranger lariat and a Lone Ranger sheriff's badge with a secret compartment, and a Tom Mix *everything*. The cowboy was king of the premiums, from spurs to a wooden

replica of the hero's own six-shooter.

Soap operas did not start with "Dallas." The thirties saw the commencement of radio soaps, some of which lasted twenty-five years. "Backstage Wife": "the story of a little Iowa girl who married Larry Nobel, handsome matinee idol, dream sweetheart of a million other women..." The mind's eye brought hyperbole nearer reality—or extended its span.

When you watch TV your eyes act as censors, quantifying everything you hear. The set is in your living room or bedroom or kitchen and you are just a glance away from the screen. But when you are in a room with a radio and it's dark and there's little distraction, a rerun of the Lone Ranger or Sherlock Holmes conjures, in total escapism, a vision personally tailored by your own perception and imagination. "Furniture that talks," one popular comedian called it. I prefer "The magic box."

Before 1950, radio shaped America like the railroad had, and then the automobile. The rail network shaped cities and our economic lives. The railroad provided the citizens of Kansas the opportunity to sell more wheat and to buy New York ready-to-wear dresses. Later the automobile moved many people to the suburbs, the postwar economy, and a new, consumer status. But radio shaped the American mind and its imagination.

In May 1949, 12 percent of the city of Baltimore watched TV. By May 1950, more than 50 percent was watching. The transition of the nature of radio programming had begun. Today, music and news are the staple. And we have it on the move, in our cars more than our homes.

When we listened at home the radio receivers were primitive objects, by today's high-tech standards, though they did the job. As technical advances improved the interior mechanism, the whole set could be made lighter and smaller. Radio design, then, plots an advancement from the cumbersome wooden consoles of the twenties and thirties to the matchbox-size receiver of today that can fit in a very small pocket. The designs featured here represent a cross section of three decades of radio cabinet aesthetics. Their elegance and sometimes whimsy is uniquely American. Very few models from overseas manufacturers could rival the imaginative appeal and flair from the U.S. companies.

The infinite variation of cabinet design over a period of thirty years offers the collector the continual prospect of finding something new, and sometimes undocumented. Vintage-radio collecting has mushroomed in the United States. To find a fifty-year-old radio that approaches mint condition is rare indeed, and treasured by the collector, but much else can be treasured and even returned to good order. There are specialists now who enjoy comfortable careers as restorers and manufacturers of replication parts, such as knobs, dial glasses, trims, handles, and cosmetic adornments that time has not treated well. Besides, discoloration and age cracks can cause effects that actually enhance rather than detract from the appeal of a plastic radio. Oxidation sometimes produces a variation of color that was never envisioned by the original designer but is prized by today's discerning collector.

The thrill of the chase where old radios are the quarry does not end with the mere discovery of an unusual set.

So hardy are they that invariably a dial light will flicker to a warm glow when the set is plugged in, and gradually the sound will phase up through forty years of dust, and the set brings forth life once more.

Many collectible sets were discarded to attics or basements not through any malfunction, but because of the consumer's desire to own the latest model. When the FM alternative band was introduced, millions of sets were replaced. (A similar revolution took place with the introduction of the color TV; early TVs are now respectable collectibles.) The passion for radio collecting has spawned vintage radio clubs in almost every American state and supports a healthy national magazine. Many prized sets have been purchased at obscure swap meets and garage sales for very little money, often before the sun has come up.

In only eleven years, between 1930 and 1941, an estimated 71 million home radio receivers were sold in the United States. I have about 350 of them. They are a pleasure to hear as well as see, today and in the mind's eye of my youth, in equal measure.

Philip Collins

9

RADIOS
R E D U X

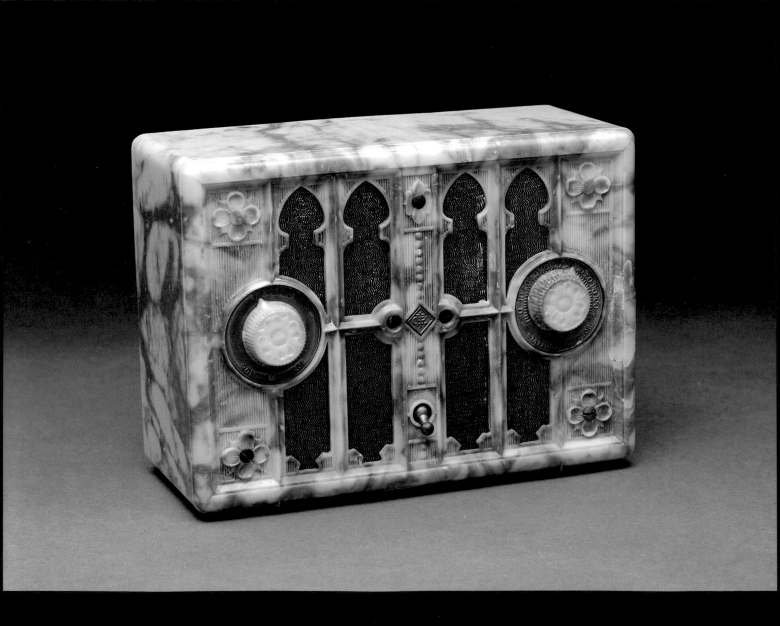

Stewart Warner "World's Fair" 1933

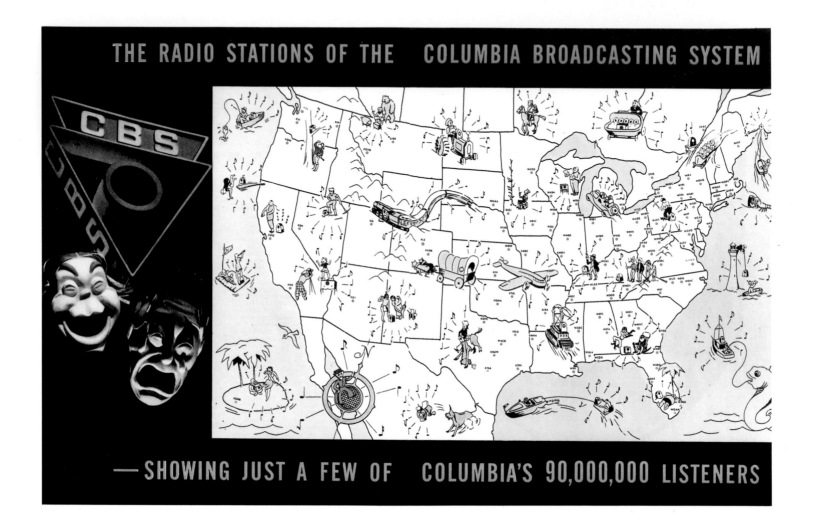

Still they Come
To the sensational 1937 Kadette Models already announced, we add . . .

The New KADETTE
Classic RADIO

JUST AS BEAUTIFUL-FRONT OR BACK

JUST AS BEAUTIFUL-FRONT OR BACK

Beauty heretofore unheard of in radio—beauty from any angle—front or back—places the new Kadette Classic high among the world's finest products.

Entirely new form, color and texture combine to produce the most beautiful compact radio of all time . . . beauty created with crystal-like translucent grilles of Tenite, set off by backgrounds of Plaskon and Bakelite in harmonious colors. Three different plastics used in radio design for the first time.

Four distinct color combinations fit the Classic into any room in any home. For the boudoir there is a particularly unusual color scheme—delicate ivory with top of canary yellow and amber grille. For the modern room there is a striking combination of black body, brilliant red top and grille in ivory. These are but two of the four color combinations—others are equally attractive.

Truly, in the realm of fine design the new Kadette Classic merits a high place.

$29.50 COMPLETE

EQUALLY BEAUTIFUL, FRONT OR BACK · · SIX TUBES · · SUPERHETERODYNE · · AC OR DC OPERATION · · ILLUMINATED ENCLOSED DIAL · · SEVERAL EFFECTIVE COLOR COMBINATIONS · · AUTOMATIC VOLUME CONTROL

On Display—Radio Exposition, Grand Central Palace, N. Y.

THE KADETTE LINE FOR 1937 COMPRISES 23 FAST-SELLING MODELS—FROM COMPACTS TO CONSOLES

INTERNATIONAL RADIO CORPORATION · 513 Williams Street · **ANN ARBOR, MICHIGAN**

18

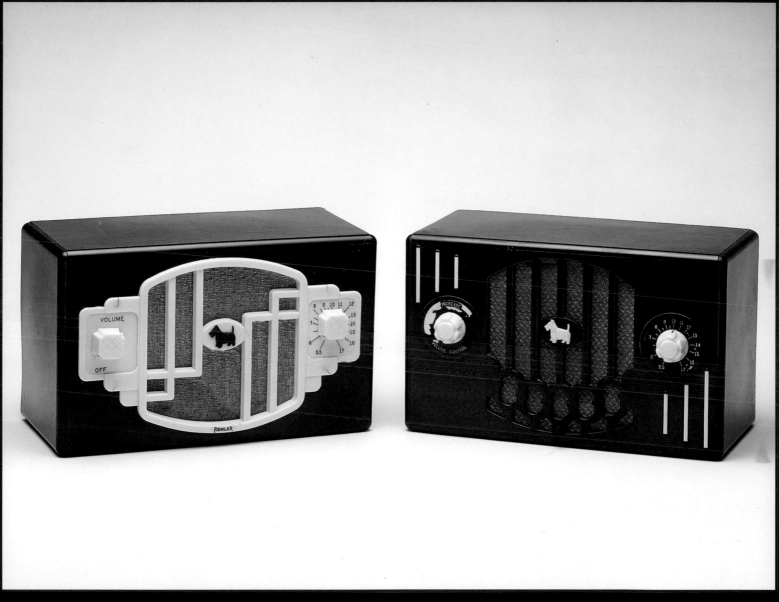

THIS IS
Today's Radio!

Communications are the lifeblood of today's war tempo . . . whether they're signaling "bombs away!" over the inter-com system of a bomber five miles above a vital target . . . or aiding a sleek sub-marine as it stalks its unsuspecting prey through the silence of the deep. That is radio today. When peace comes, with it will come greater FADA skills developed by wartime lessons . . . devoted to the production of FADA radios with hitherto undreamed-of tonal faithfulness, per-formance and durability.

PLACE YOUR FAITH IN THE

FADA *Radio*

OF THE FUTURE

Famous Since Broadcasting Began!

FADA RADIO AND ELECTRIC COMPANY, INC.. LONG ISLAND CITY, N. Y.

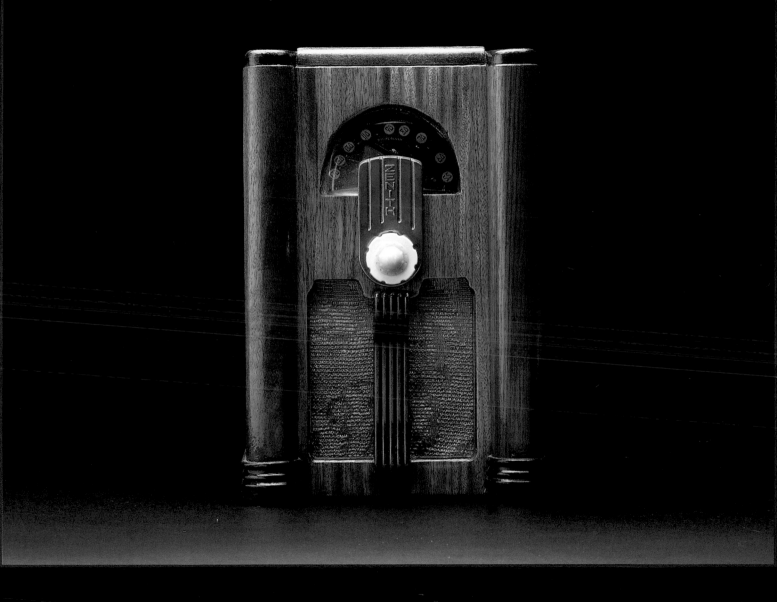

Detrola "Pee Wee" 1938   **31**

"HIS MASTER'S VOICE"... the history of a famous Trade Mark

1   "His Master's Voice"

T. M. Reg. U. S. Pat. Off.

2 "Hello! Lots of people don't know it but my name is NIPPER. I was a real dog who really recognized 'His Master's Voice' back in 1898."

3 "But what made me immortal, was that my master (a painter fellow named Francis Barraud) caught sight of me listening one day . . ."

4 "And then I had to do the hardest work of my life—posing! If there's one thing I don't like to do, it's to sit still . . . But I did it for hours!"

5 "Then they took Mr. Barraud's painting of me and ran it as a Victrola* advertisement . . . I was started on my career to world fame!"

ONLY RCA VICTOR MAKES THE VICTROLA*

* "Victrola"—T.M. Reg. U.S Pat. Off.

6 "Next, another kind of 'music box' came along—a radio made by RCA. Then when RCA merged with Victor—in 1929, I became even more famous!"

7 "So today you have something that never was dreamed of! You have the real-life TONE of the new RCA Victor 'Golden Throat.'"

"There are four table radios—including a set with short wave that can 'pull in' stations 12,000 miles away! And a battery radio you can plug in and run on AC if you want to. MY favorite is the 'Personal'—it's the tiniest, neatest portable RCA Victor ever made!

"Then, there's an automatic radio-phonograph that's nearly 1/3 smaller than the prewar table model. And, two console radios that make 'His Master's Voice' more real than ever."

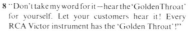

8 "Don't take my word for it—hear the 'Golden Throat' for yourself. Let your customers hear it! Every RCA Victor instrument has the 'Golden Throat'!"

RCA   **RCA VICTOR**

RADIO CORPORATION OF AMERICA

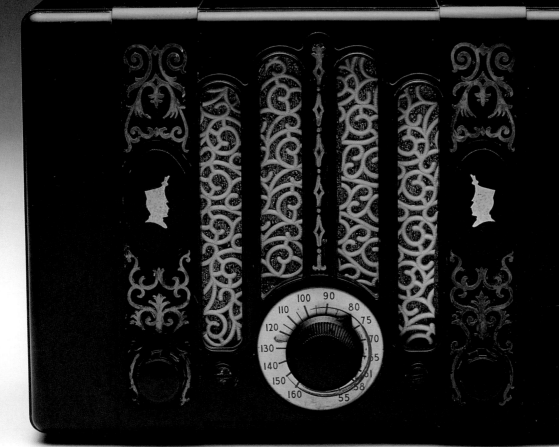

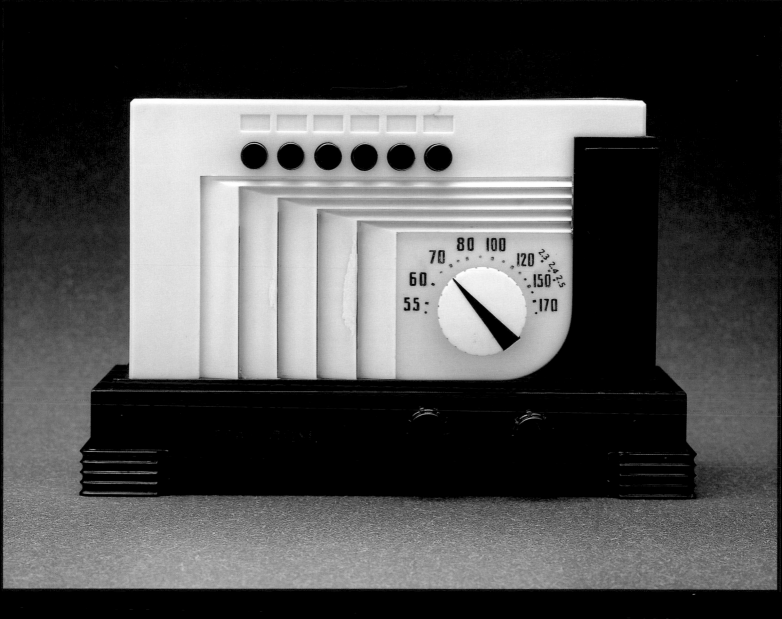

Philco "Transitone" c. 1938 **39**

★ CHARLIE McCARTHY'S RADIO PARTY ★

DIRECTIONS AND RULES FOR PLAYING

1. The game consists of 21 figures... one of Charlie McCarthy and four each of Edgar Bergen, Don Ameche, Dorothy Lamour, Nelson Eddy and Robert Armbruster. Also a spinner which determines the play.

2. The game is won by the player who first secures *one* of each of the figures (no duplicates) including Charlie McCarthy, or when a player gets all of the figures (20) without Charlie McCarthy.

3. To start, all figures are arranged in individual groups face up in the center of the table.

4. Players spin. The one getting the highest number starts the game. If two or more persons get the same high number, they spin until tie is broken. Order of play is clockwise from the first player.

5. The game is played by spinning the pointer and following the directions given in the box on which arrow stops. If the arrow stops exactly on the line separating two boxes the player spins again.

6. If a player is unable to complete the play specified, player must pass.

7. Figures taken by a player are placed, face up, in front of him.

8. Each play is completed when player releases figure selected.

9. Pointer must make at least one complete revolution.

10. In making an exchange the player must exchange his figure for a different figure.

11. The figure of Charlie McCarthy is moved only when so specified by pointer.

The Charlie McCarthy Radio Game is fascinating and requires a certain amount of skill in playing. While the object is to secure a full set of figures, a player should constantly maneuver his plays so that he will prevent his opponents securing a complete set.

"Roger"

Nothing could be more welcome to the weary pilot as he prepares to land than that cheery "Roger" from the control tower assuring him that all is well and he may come in. One more mission completed . . . one more hazardous job well done!

That's the FADA *contribution of today* . . . making the dangerous business of war just a little safer for our courageous fighting men through electronic devices and radio equipment.

Tomorrow—the word "FADA" will be a cheery symbol of the finest in peacetime radio and electronic developments. Tomorrow, our dealers will be guided to new heights of profit by FADA achievements in the field of communications.

PLACE YOUR FAITH IN THE

OF THE FUTURE

Famous Since Broadcasting Began!

FADA RADIO AND ELECTRIC COMPANY, INC., LONG ISLAND CITY, N. Y.

48 "General" c. 1939

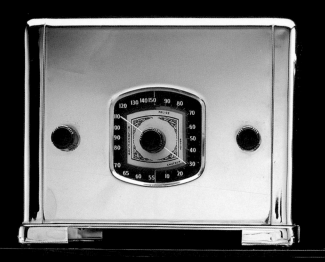

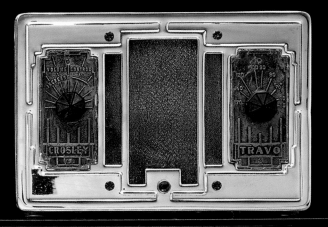

50   Detrola c. 1939

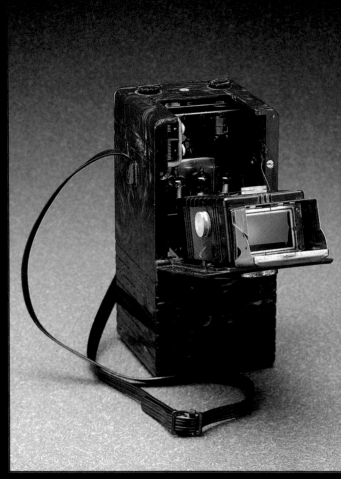

56   Hamilton Ross "Camera Radio" 1942

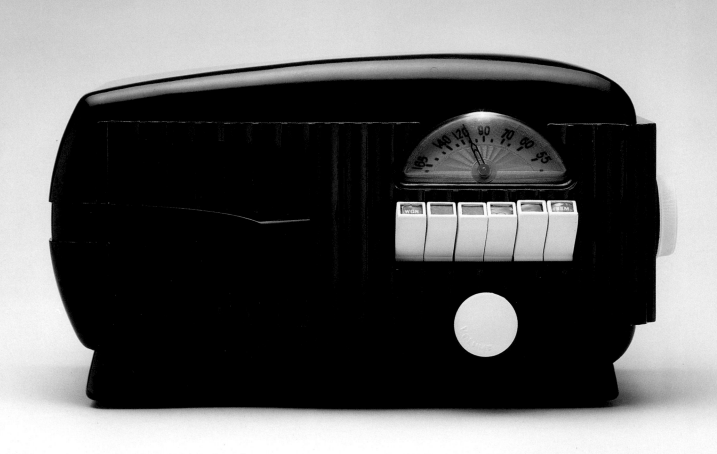

"Miniature Miracle"

WORLD'S SMALLEST, "POWER-PACKED" AC-DC SUPERHETERODYNE

Emerson Radio has done it again! FIRST-and-smallest — with modern engineering to utilize war-born developments of miniature tubes! FIRST to compose the latest and most efficient electronic developments in light "palm-of-your-hand" AC-DC Super-heterodyne radio with super power.

Consider the tube complement alone! 1 type 12BE6, 1 type 12BA6, 1 type 12AT6, 1 type 50B5, 1 rectifier 35W4. Wide range of colors available.

Here is merchandising NEWS—here is a compact, beautiful, lightweight little set that EVERYONE will want, regardless of how many other sets they may have—for any room in the house, for traveling, for a gift—and ONLY

Model 540 WALNUT PLASTIC $19⁹⁵

Ask Your Emerson Radio Distributor

Demand for Emerson Radio Model 540 is skyrocketing. Telephone or wire your Emerson distributor now.

Emerson
Radio and Television

THE NEW 1947
Emerson Radio

BACKED BY A NATIONWIDE PROMOTION CAMPAIGN

Nationally — locally — and at point-of-sale — the advertising and sales promotion of the "Miniature Miracle" is as outstanding as the set itself. Tie in with this business-building drive. Make it your PROMOTION LEADER for 1947.

EMERSON RADIO AND PHONOGRAPH CORPORATION • NEW YORK 11, N. Y.
World's Largest Maker of Small Radio

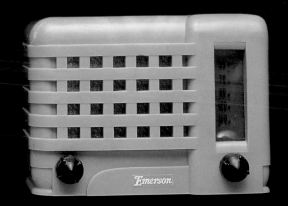

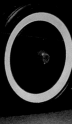
radio flyer _____ 7

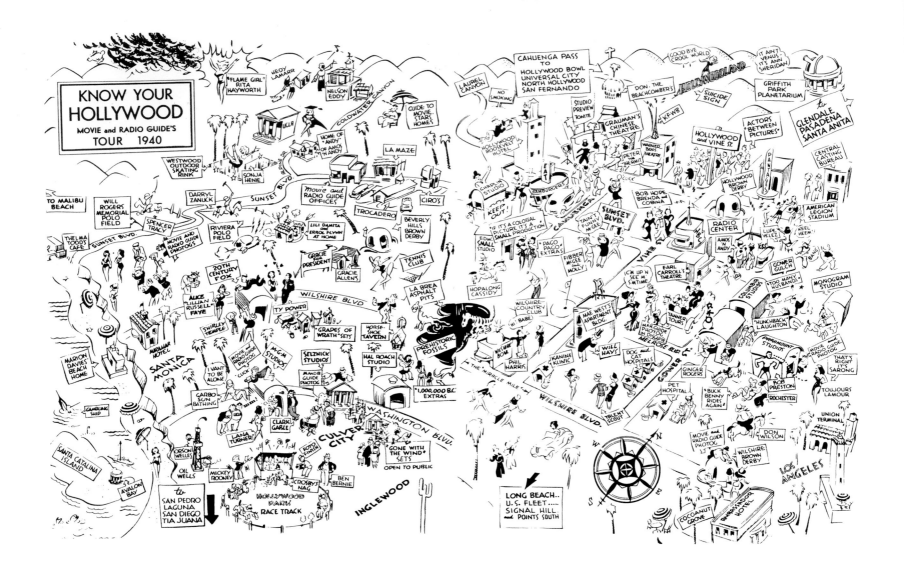

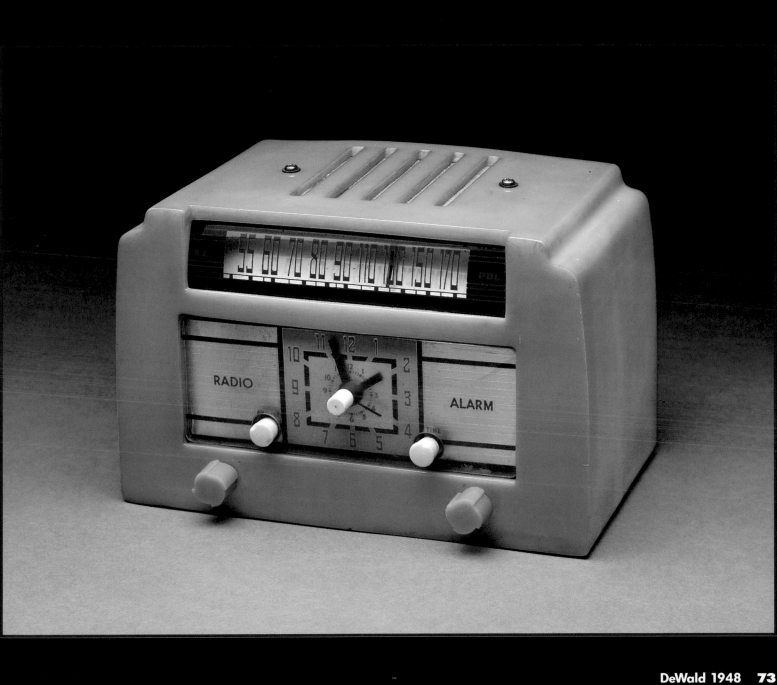

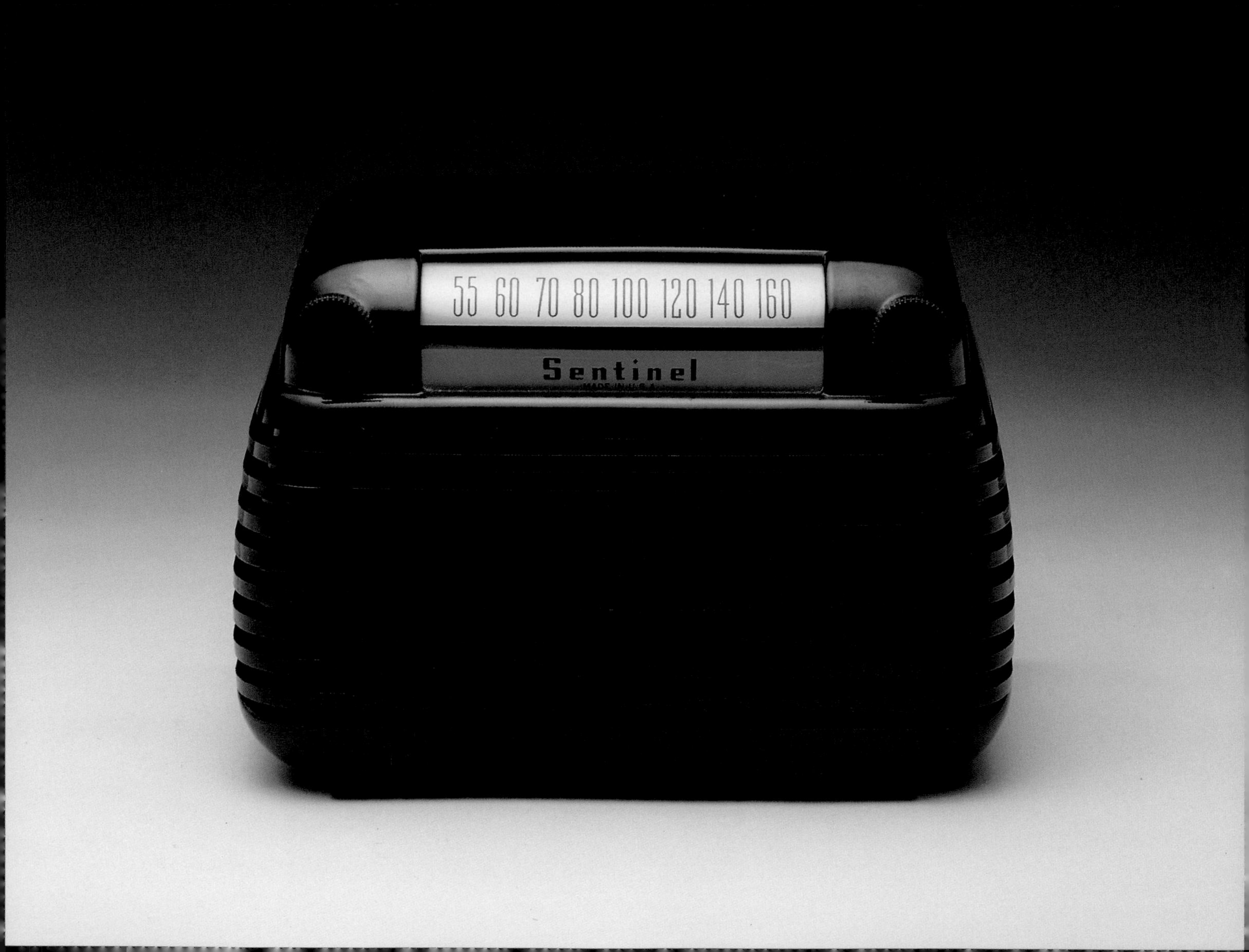
55 60 70 80 100 120 140 160
Sentinel

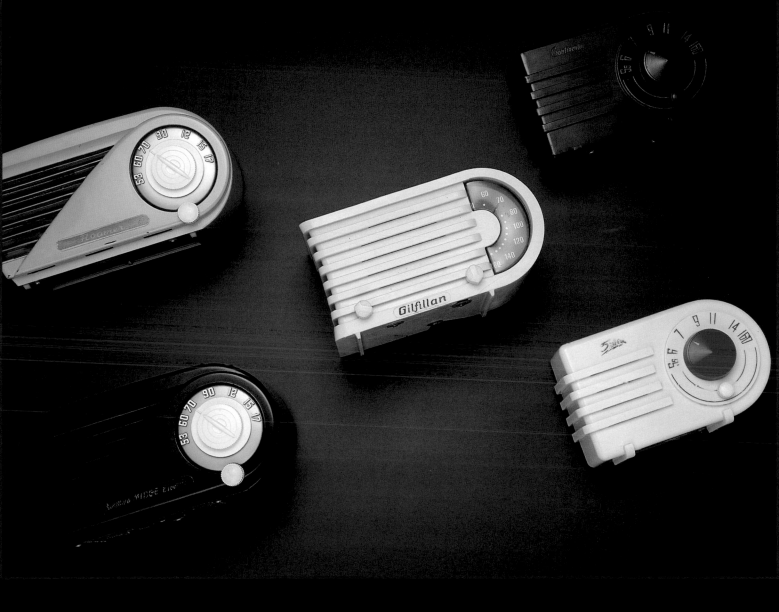

New *Motorola*® Calendar Clock Radio

Sings you to sleep at night

(THEN SHUTS ITSELF OFF)

Sings you awake in the morning

Tells you the time, the day and the date—all for just $39.95*

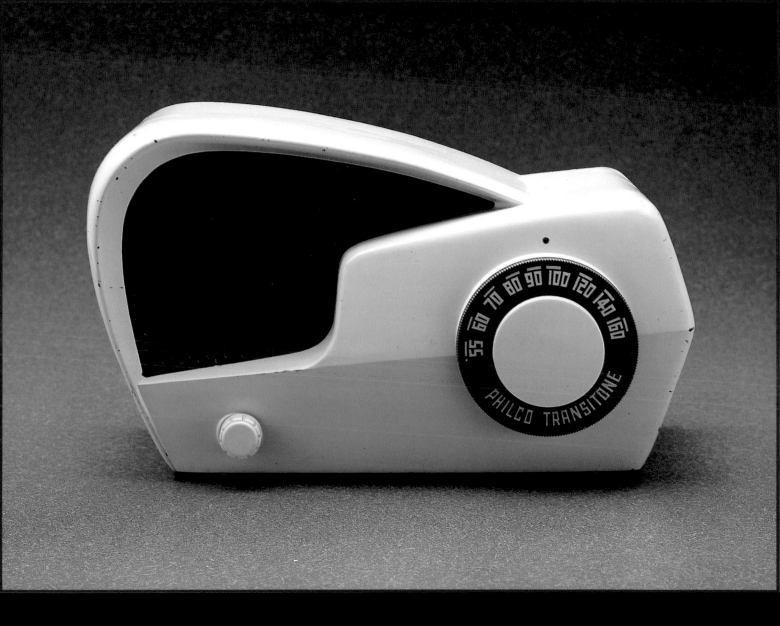

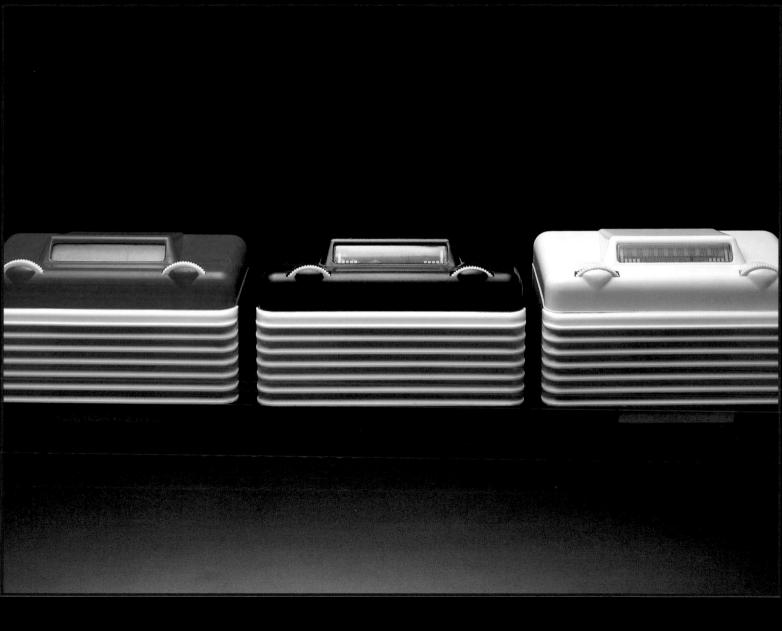

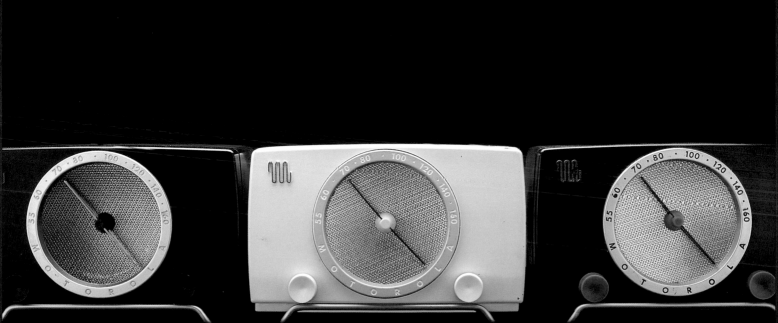

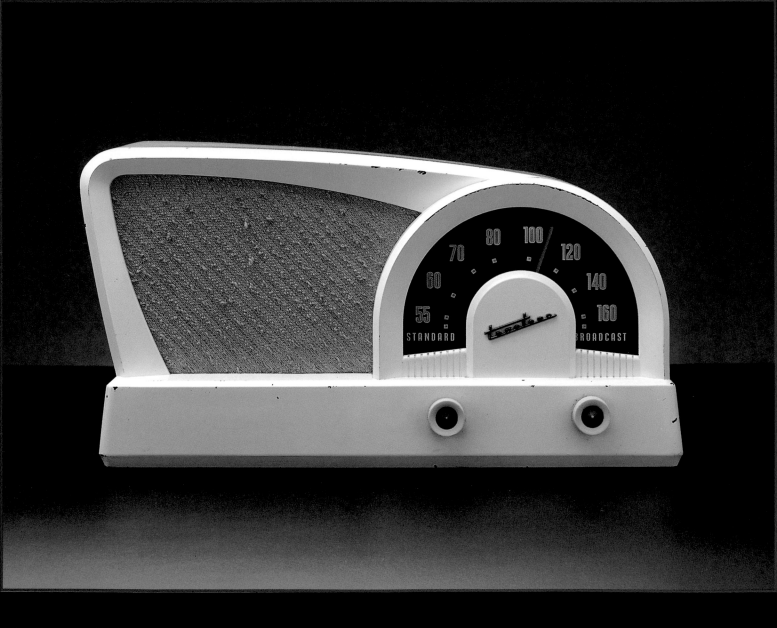

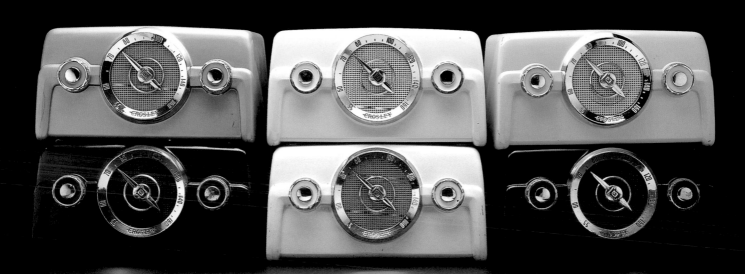

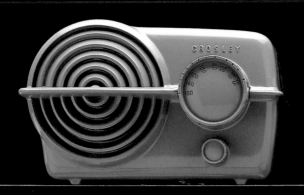
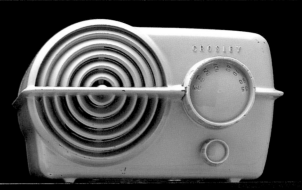

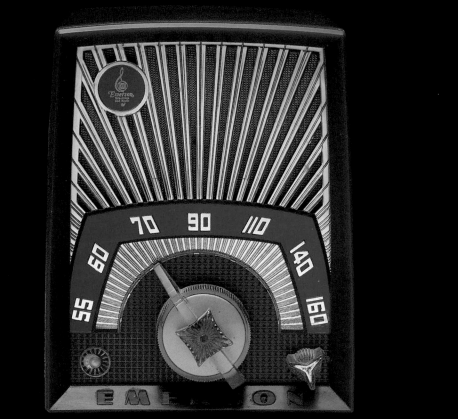

NEW

— the biggest little handfuls
of tone quality ZENITH ever made

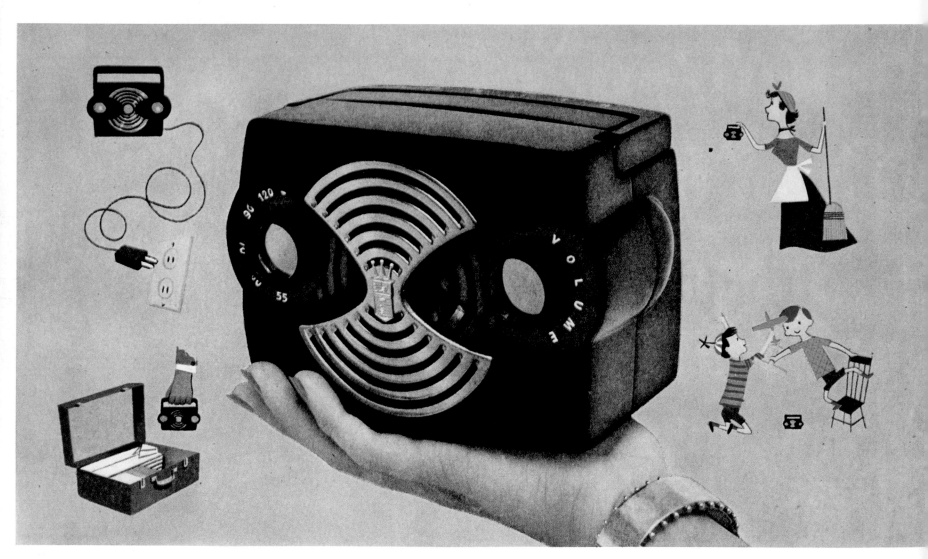

Motorola (left and right) 1953 and Philco "Transitone" 1952   **95**

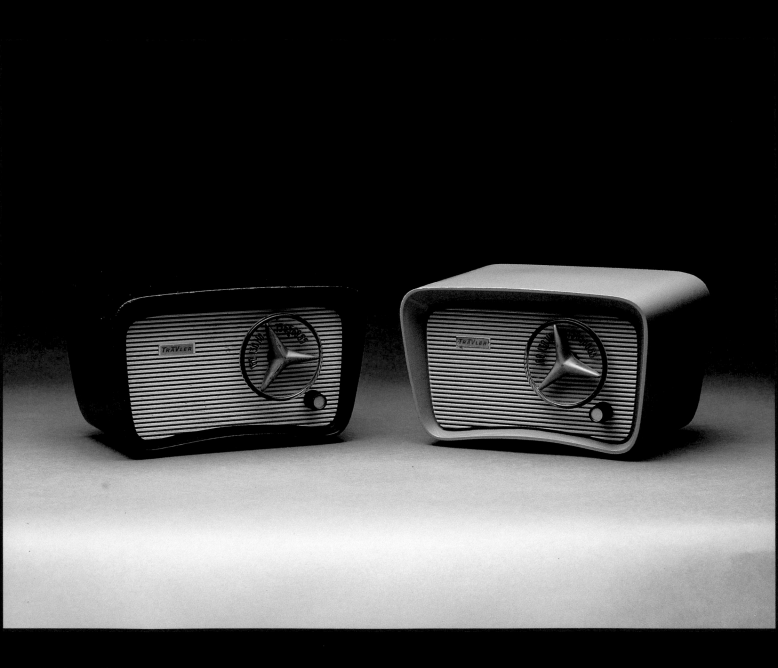

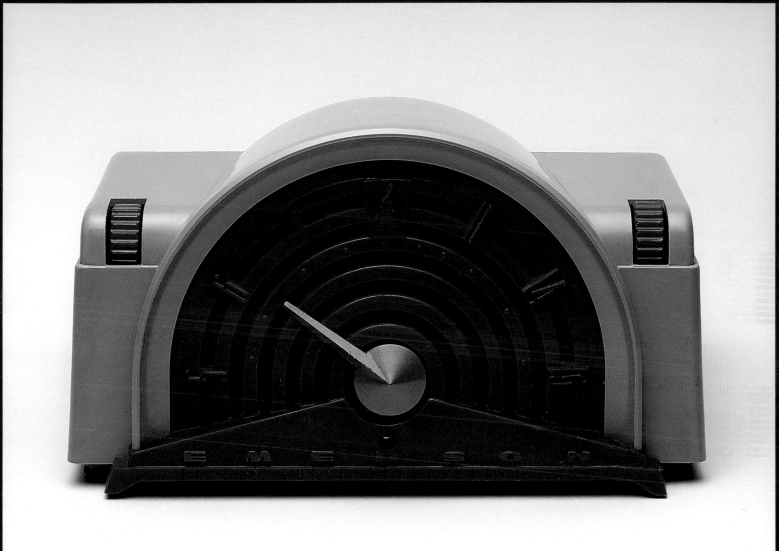

98   Zenith c. 1955

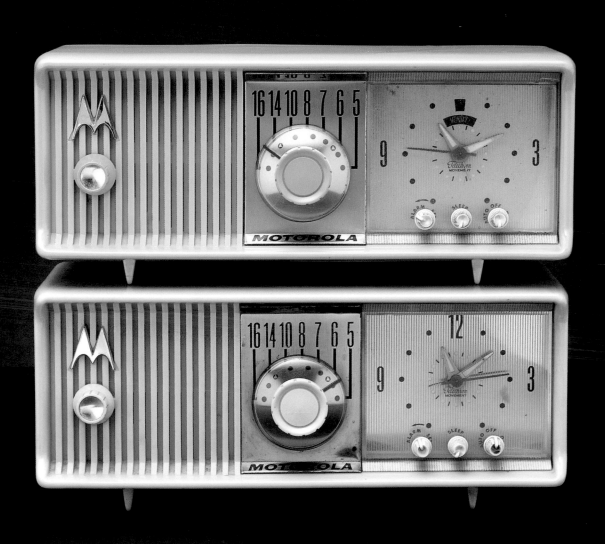

12 International Kadette: *1932*
The first plastic cabinet radio
Philip Collins Collection

17 Stewart Warner *"Good Companion"*
Model R-192: *1936*
Metal cabinet
Chrome pillars
Klaus Beckmann Collection

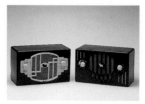

21 Remler "Scottie"
Left: Model 40: 1936
Right: Model 26: c. 1936

13 Stewart Warner *"World's Fair"*
Model R-108: *1933*
"A Century of Progress" special design
Metal
Philip Collins Collection

19 Kadette *"Classic"*: *1936*
Top left: Model K14
Top right: Model K16
Bottom left: Model K13
Bottom right: Model K10
Victor Keen Collection

23 Fada *Model 246G: 1937*
Philip Collins Collection

14/15 Radio Glo c. *1935*
Glass and chromed metal on a wood base
Courtesy Harvey's, Melrose Avenue, Los Angeles

20 Kadette "Classic"
Back view

24 Pilot *"Lone Ranger"* Model G-160:
c. *1937*
Wood
Kris Gimmy Collection

25 Zenith *Model 6D326: 1938*
Bruce and Tina Herman Collection

28 Emerson *"Snow White" Model DB 247:*
1938
Wood and pressed wood (Syroco) facing
Barry and Ellen Blum Collection

32 Silvertone *Model 6110: 1938*
Designed by Clarence Karstadt
Refinished
Philip Collins Collection

26 Silvertone *c. 1938*
Philip Collins Collection

29 Emerson *"Snow White" Model Q 236:*
1938
Wood
Jerry Simpson Collection

33 Stewart Warner *"Dionne Quints"*
Model 07-513Q: 1938
Philip Collins Collection

27 Silvertone *Model 6178A: c. 1938*
Philip Collins Collection

30/31 Detrola *"Pee Wee": 1938*
Left: Model 284
Center: Model 199
Right: Model 219
Designed by George Walker
Philip Collins Collection

35 RCA *c. 1938*
Export model from Chile
Philip Collins Collection

36 International Kadette *Model 150: 1938*
Philip Collins Collection

39 Philco "Transitone" Model: UA 52P
c. 1938
Restored
New tuning dial
Philip Collins Collection

45 RCA "World's Fair" Model 40 x 56: 1939
Pressed wood facing
Wood cabinet
Bruce and Charlotte Mager Collection

37 Silvertone *Model 3251: c. 1938*
Philip Collins Collection

43 Fada Model L-56: 1939
Designed by Frederick E. Greene
Philip Collins Collection

46 Belmont *Model 521A: 1939*
Philip Collins Collection

38 *Top left:* Automatic Model 614X: 1946
Top right: Fada Model 454: 1938
Bottom left: Bendix Model 111: 1948
Bottom right: Airline Model 93 BR
509A: c. 1940
Philip Collins Collection

44 RCA "San Francisco Expo"
Model 40 x 57: 1939
Pressed wood facing
Wood cabinet
Bruce and Charlotte Mager Collection

47 General Electric: 1939
Left: Model H500
Center: Model H500
Right: Model H502
Philip Collins Collection
Center: Bill and Connie Cawfield Collection

48 "General" c. 1939
Chromed metal
Wood
Rubber
Bruce and Charlotte Mager Collection

49 *Top left:* Perwal Model #52: 1937
Top right: Crosley "Travo" 166: 1933
Bottom left: Arvin Model 522A: 1941
Bottom right: Sparton: c. 1940
Metal chromed
Philip Collins Collection

50 Detrola *Model 302:* c. 1939
Mirror facing
Wood cabinet
Kris Gimmy Collection

51 RCA *"La Siesta" Model 40 x 53:* 1939
Wood
Barry and Ellen Blum Collection

52 Kadette *"Topper"* Model L-25: 1940
Bambi and David Mednick Collection

53 Radio Vision *Model 414:* 1940
Wood
Heat from an illuminated bulb generates the
rotation of a translucent cylinder giving an illusion
of movement to the image.
Kris Gimmy Collection

54 Trophy *"Bowling Ball"* c. 1941
Bruce and Charlotte Mager Collection

55 Tinymite c. 1940
Crystal Receiver
Philip Collins Collection

56 Hamilton Ross *"Camera Radio":* 1942
Plastic and metal
Kris Gimmy Collection

57 Detrola *Model 568-1: 1946*
Chromed metal
Philip Collins Collection

60 Remler *Model MP5-5-3: 1946*
Philip Collins Collection

63 Silvertone *Model 3561: 1947*
Philip Collins Collection

58 Majestic *Model 52: c. 1946*
Philip Collins Collection

61 Remler: *1947*
Left: Model 5506
Right: Model 5500
Philip Collins Collection

64/65 Remler *Model 5300: 1947*
Philip Collins Collection

59 Airline *Model 62-455: 1946*
Philip Collins Collection

62 Airline *Model 84BR 1508B: 1946*
Kay Tornborg Collection

67 Emerson *Model 540: 1947*
Philip Collins Collection

**68 Emerson "Moderne" Model 517 Series:
1947**
Philip Collins Collection

72 Delco Model R-1238: 1948
Philip Collins Collection

75 *Top left:* Northern Electric "Roamer"
Model 5508: c. 1948
Top right: Continental Model 44: c. 1950
Center: Gilfillan Model 58M: 1948
Bottom left: Northern Electric "Midge"
Model L660: c. 1948
Bottom right: Shellern Model 44: c. 1950
Philip Collins Collection

69 Motorola Model 55 x 15: 1947
The Mother's Day radio
Philip Collins Collection

73 DeWald Model B512: 1948
Philip Collins Collection

71 "Hollywood" c. 1948
Refinished Grill
Philip Collins Collection

74 Sentinel Model 314W: 1948
Philip Collins Collection

**76 Northern Electric Model 5002 Series
c. 1948**
Philip Collins Collection

77 DeWald "Bantam" Model B401: 1948
Philip Collins Collection

81 *Top left:* Lone Ranger flashlight: *1948*
Top center: Roy Rogers microscope: *1949*
Top right: Sky King Magna-Glo writing: *1949*
Center left to right: Captain Midnight
Sliding Secret Compartment: *194*
Lone Ranger Weather Detector: *1947*
Straight Arrow Gold Nugget Picture: *1950*
Buck Rogers Ring of Saturn: *1944*
Bottom left to right:
Frank Buck Explorers Sun Dial: *1949*
Lone Ranger Hike-O-Meter: *1948*
Popsicle Boot: *1951*
Bill and Connie Cawfield Collection

83 Setchell Carlson Model 416: c. 1950
Center and right: Philip Collins Collection
Left: Barry and Ellen Blum Collection

79 Philco "Transitone" Model 49-501: 1949
Philip Collins Collection

84 Sterling "Deluxe" c. 1950
Philip Collins Collection

80 *Top left:* Sky Kings Teleblinker: *1951*
Top right: Gabby Hayes Shooting Cannon: *1951*
Center left to right: Lone Ranger Atomic Bomb: *1946*
Terry and the Pirates Gold Detector: *1947*
Lone Ranger Movie Film Viewer: *1949*
Tom Mix Sliding Whistle: *1949*
Bottom left: Lone Ranger Six Shooter: *1948*
Captain Video Space Gun: *1950*
Bill and Connie Cawfield Collection

82 Philco "Transitone" Model 49-503: 1949
Philip Collins Collection

85 Motorola
Left: Model 5 x 13U
Center: Model 5 x 12U
Right: Model 5 x 11U
Designed by Jean Otis Reinecke
Bakelite cabinet
Metal trim
Philip Collins Collection

86 Truetone *Model D2018: 1950*
Philip Collins Collection

89 Crosley *Models 11-114 thru 11-118U: 1951*
Barry and Ellen Blum Collection
(top left and right, bottom right)
Philip Collins Collection (center & bottom left)

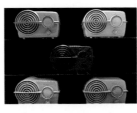

93 Zenith "Crest" *Model K-4129: 1952*
Philip Collins Collection

87 Crosley *Models 10-135 thru 10-140: 1950*
Barry and Ellen Blum Collection
Bakelite cabinet
Metal knobs and trim
(top center and right)
Philip Collins Collection (top left and bottom row)

90 Emerson *Model 707B: 1952*
Sunburst design
Philip Collins Collection

94/95 *Left:* Motorola Model 53H: 1953
Center: Philco "Transitone" Model: 548-M: 1952
Right: Motorola Model 53HH: 1953
Philip Collins Collection

88 Midgetronic *Model EMU 4214: 1950*
English
Sandy Lieberson Collection

91 RCA Pepsi Cooler *Model PCR-5: 1952*
Jerry Simson Collection

96 TraVler *Model 2160: c. 1954*
Philip Collins Collection

113

97 Emerson *Model 744-B: 1954*
Philip Collins Collection

100 Motorola *Model 57R: 1957*
Philip Collins Collection

103 Motorola *Model 5T13P: 1959*
Metal cabinet housing
Philip Collins Collection

98 Zenith c. *1955*
Left: Model T402
Center: Model T400
Right: Model M403
Barry and Ellen Blum Collection

101 Motorola
Top: Model 57 CC: 1957
Bottom: Model 56 CD 1956
Philip Collins Collection

99 Motorola *Model 56H: 1956*
Philip Collins Collection

102 Silvertone c. *1959*
Left: Model 8218
Right: Model 8219
Barry and Ellen Blum Collection

NOTES:

Unless otherwise stated, cabinets are molded from a variety of phenolic resins, the most popular being Bakelite and Plaskon. Hundreds of plastic compound variations were used by the molding companies, which sometimes produced the same model radio in two or three different plastic types.

All models featured are in original condition unless described otherwise. The date refers to the first year of production of the generic design. A popular radio sometimes sold for many years with minor cosmetic or technical changes. To a discerning collector, a change in dial face design or knob color is important and contributes to the enjoyment of finding something different and new. The many variations in design contribute significantly to the pleasure of collecting these magic boxes.

PHOTOGRAPHER'S NOTES:

The photographs in this book were shot at the El Royale Studio in Los Angeles. Fuji film and a Fuji 6 × 8 medium format camera were used exclusively. Dynalite 1000 watt strobes were mounted in a variety of chimera soft boxes. In several cases multiple flashes from the strobe lights were needed to provide the correct exposure at F-32. In order to obtain illumination on the radio dials, exposures from 15 seconds to 3 minutes were used.

Sam Sargent

INDEX OF MODELS

ACKNOWLEDGMENTS:

Grateful thanks are due to all the collectors who kindly contributed their sets for inclusion in this book. Special mention to:

Baron Wolman

Sam Sargent

Mary Merrick

Kay Tornborg

Jerry Simpson

Victor Kean

Bill Cawlfield

Pro Vision—San Francisco

RC Vintage—LA

Harvey Schwartz

PERMISSIONS:

Emerson "Miniature Miracle" advertisement: Courtesy Emerson Radio Corp.

Zenith "Crest" advertisement: Courtesy Zenith Radio Corp.

"His Master's Voice" T/M advertisement: Courtesy Radio Corporation of America Inc.

Charley McCarthy's Radio Party (Text): Courtesy Standard Brands Inc.

"See You On The Radio": Courtesy THE OSGOOD FILE, CBS NEWS RADIO. Copyrighted by CBS Inc. All rights reserved.